grade
1

For full details of exam requireme[nts] current syllabus in conjunctio[n] *Information & Regulations* and th[e] teachers and parents, *These Musi[c]* .... These three documents are available online at www.abrsm.org, as well as free of charge from music retailers, from ABRSM local representatives or from the Services Department, The Associated Board of the Royal Schools of Music, 24 Portland Place, London W1B 1LU, United Kingdom.

CONTENTS AND TRACK LISTING

Track   *page*

LIST A

Track	No.	Composer	Page
1	1	**William Duncombe** Gavot: from *First Book of Progressive Lessons*	2
2	2	**Johann Philipp Kirnberger** (1721–83) Minuetto	3
3	3	**Antonio Vivaldi** (1678–1741) L'autunno: from *Le quattro stagioni*, arr. Pam Wedgwood	4

LIST B

Track	No.	Composer	Page
7	1	**Thomas Dunhill** (1877–1946) A Song of Erin: No. 8 from *First Year Pieces*	5
8	2	**Aleksandr Fyodorovich Gedike** (1877–1957) Kummer: No. 39 from *60 leichte Klavierstücke*, Op. 36	6
9	3	**Trad. English** Early one morning, arr. Carol Barratt	7

LIST C

Track	No.	Composer	Page
13	1	**Árpád Balázs** Trudging	8
14	2	**Paul Drayton** Never Vex a Tyrannosaurus Rex!	9
15	3	**John Rowcroft** African Dance	10

Where appropriate, pieces in this album have been checked with original source material and edited as necessary for instructional purposes. Fingering, metronome marks and the editorial realization of ornaments (where given) are for guidance only; they are not comprehensive or obligatory.

Editor for the Associated Board: **Richard Jones**

Alternative pieces for this grade

LIST A

Track	No.		
4	4	**Gläser** Angloise. No. 11 from *Clavierstücke für Anfänger* (Schott/MDS)	
5	5	**Handel** March in G, HWV 419³. No. 7 from Handel, *Easy Piano Pieces and Dances* (Bärenreiter)	
6	6	**Purcell** Minuet in A minor, Z. 649. No. 1 from *A Keyboard Anthology*, Third Series, Book 1 or No. 15 from *Baroque Keyboard Pieces*, Book 1 or No. 10 from *English Keyboard Music 1663–1702* (ABRSM Publishing)	

LIST B

Track	No.		
10	† 4	**Dvořák** Cavatina: No. 1 from *Miniatures* (Op. 75a). *Simply Classics*, Grades 0–1, arr. Gritton (Faber)	
11	5	**Marjorie Helyer** Dragonflies: from *The Greenwood Tree* (Stainer & Bell)	
12	† 6	**Schubert** Theme from the 'Unfinished' Symphony. *Piano Time Classics*, arr. Hall (OUP)	

LIST C

Track	No.		
16	4	**Chen Yi** Singing in the Mountain. *Spectrum 4: An International Collection of 66 Miniatures for Solo Piano* (ABRSM Publishing)	
17	5	**Alan Haughton** Bluemerang. *Piano Time Going Places*, arr. Hall (OUP)	
18	6	**Kabalevsky** My Stubborn Little Brother: from *35 Pieces for Piano*, Op. 89. *Gradations* (Boosey & Hawkes/MDS) or *Keynotes*, Grades 1–2 (Faber)	

† = this arrangement only

© 2008 by The Associated Board of the Royal Schools of Music

No part of this publication may be copied or reproduced in any form or by any means without the prior permission of the publisher.

Music origination by Barnes Music Engraving Ltd
Cover by Økvik Design
Printed in England by Halstan & Co. Ltd, Amersham, Bucks.

Gavot

from *First Book of Progressive Lessons*

DUNCOMBE

A:1

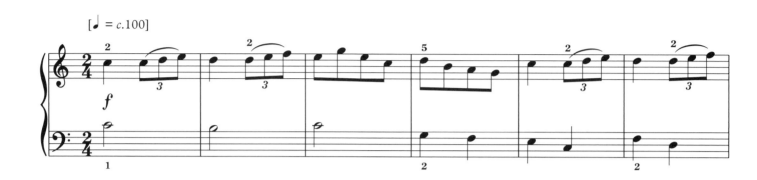

Little is known of William Duncombe beyond the fact that he lived in London in the late 18th century and was organist of St Dunstan's, Highgate. His publications include two anthologies for students of the keyboard. Many of the contents are arrangements by Duncombe of already existing pieces – some traditional, others contemporary – rather than original compositions; and this may be true of the piece selected here. 'Gavot' is an old English spelling of *gavotte*, a French dance of the 17th and 18th centuries in moderate duple time. Crotchets might be lightly detached.
Source: *First Book of Progressive Lessons for the Harpsichord and Piano Forte* (London: J. Bland, 1778)

Minuetto

A:2

KIRNBERGER

Johann Philipp Kirnberger (1721–83) studied with J. S. Bach in Leipzig from 1739 to 1741, entered the service of Princess Anna Amalia of Prussia in 1758, and later became one of the most important music theorists of his day. He advocated the study of keyboard dances to help students to develop a good sense of time and rhythm. 'Minuetto' is Italian for *minuet*, a dance in moderate triple time that originated in 17th-century France but later became popular throughout Europe. In this Minuetto, all slurs and dynamics are editorial suggestions only. Crotchets might be lightly detached.

AB 3386

L'autunno

from *Le quattro stagioni*

Arranged by
Pam Wedgwood

VIVALDI

L'autunno Autumn; **Le quattro stagioni** The Four Seasons

The popular set of four concertos entitled *Le quattro stagioni* by the Italian composer Antonio Vivaldi (1678–1741), scored for solo violin, strings and continuo, was first published in 1725 as the first four items in his Op. 8 collection of concertos. The piece selected here is a keyboard arrangement by Pam Wedgwood of the finale of 'L'autunno' (Concerto in F, Op. 8 No. 3, RV 293), which depicts the hunt. The original is in 3/8 time.

AB 3386

A Song of Erin

No. 8 from *First Year Pieces*

B:1

DUNHILL

Andante con moto [♩ = *c*.120]

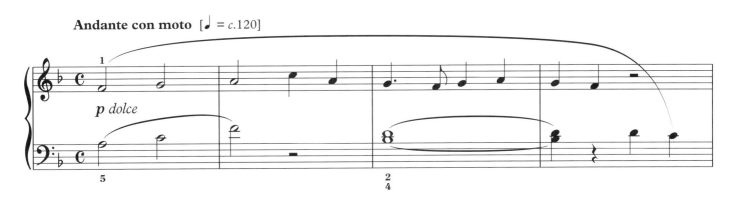

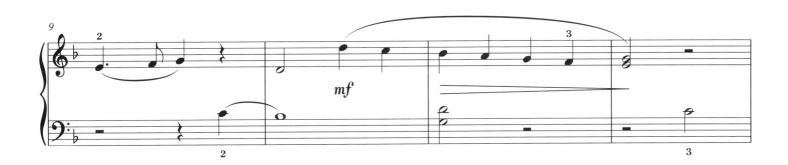

poco rit.

The English composer Thomas Dunhill (1877–1946) studied composition with Stanford at the Royal College of Music, where he himself later taught. He wrote a large quantity of music for educational purposes. 'Erin' in the title of this piece is a poetic name for Ireland, and the music has something of the character of Irish traditional music.

B:2

Kummer

No. 39 from *60 leichte Klavierstücke*, Op. 36

GEDIKE

Kummer Grief; **60 leichte Klavierstücke** 60 Easy Piano Pieces

Aleksandr Fyodorovich Gedike (1877–1957) was a Russian composer and pianist who studied at the Moscow Conservatory and later became professor of piano there. He appeared both in Russia and abroad as a concert pianist. This piece is drawn from the collection of 60 easy piano pieces for beginners that Gedike published in 1927.
Source: *60 leichte Klavierstücke für Anfänger*, Op. 36 (Moscow, Vienna and Leipzig, 1927)

Early one morning

B:3

Arranged by
Carol Barratt

TRAD. ENGLISH

This piece is a piano arrangement of a traditional English song, whose first verse reads:

    Early one morning, just as the sun was rising,
    I heard a maid sing in the valley below:
    'Oh, don't deceive me; Oh, never leave me!
    How could you use a poor maiden so?'

AB 3386

Trudging

ÁRPÁD BALÁZS

Árpád Balázs is a Hungarian composer who was born in 1937 and studied in Budapest and Rome. His compositions include seven stage works, two oratorios, 15 orchestral works and 200 pieces for choir. For three years he presented a successful series about classical music on Hungarian television.

Never Vex a Tyrannosaurus Rex! C:2

PAUL DRAYTON

This piece is drawn from the collection *Prehistoric Piano Time* by Pauline Hall and Paul Drayton (b. 1944), in which it is accompanied by the following cautionary note: 'Tyrannosaurus Rex is quite alright if left alone, but if teased it can be terrifying.'

AB 3386

African Dance

JOHN ROWCROFT

John Rowcroft (b. 1970) is a classically trained British composer who mainly writes and produces music for film and television. His *Bigger Picture Piano* series, from which this piece is drawn, explores a range of jazz and pop styles. 'African Dance' is in a South African 'township' style – relaxed yet with crisply articulated rhythms. An acceptable tempo for this piece in the exam would be ♩ = *c*.100.